Pa

GW00984640

1

Pat naps.

Pip pats Pat.

Pat naps.

Pip taps Pat.

Pat naps.

Pip tips Pat.

Pat naps.

Pip taps a pan.

Pat naps!

Who are these characters?

Pip   Pat

Can you read these words?

pan   nap   mat   dip

Spelling and writing

Ask your child to blend and read the words below. Ask them to say each word and to tap out the phonemes (sounds) of the word with their fingers. Then ask your child to try writing each word.

in

at

tin

Understanding the story

These questions will help you to check that your child understands the story.

1 Where is Pat? (page 2)

2 What does Pip do? (page 3)